Help Annie Apple to draw some more apples on her tree.
How many can you draw?

Bb

Help Bouncy Ben to find his bright blue ball.
Colour the butterflies.

Help Clever Cat by drawing some more candles on her cake. Colour the cake.

Dd

Help Dippy Duck to draw the dog by joining the dots.
Colour the dog.

Eddy Elephant loves Easter eggs. Draw two more eggs and colour all of them.

Ff

Fireman Fred and his friends are having fun fishing. Who has caught a fish?

Golden Girl has a lovely garden. Can you find her glasses? Colour the grass and the gate green.

Gg

Hh

Help the Hairy Hat Man and his friends to hunt for eight hidden hats.

Impy Ink's insect friends have been having fun. Where has each insect come from? Colour the puddles.

I i

J j

Help Jumping Jim to finish the jigsaw. Only one piece fits. Join it to the jigsaw with a line.

Kicking King likes keys.
Which two keys are the same?
Colour the kittens.

Kk

Ll

Lucy Lamp Lady is looking for five lost lambs. Circle each lamb. Draw a line to show the way to the lighthouse.

Munching Mike is mopping up the mess. Five things are missing in the bottom picture. Can you find them?

Nn

Naughty Nick has nine nails. How many has he bent? Draw some more nails for him to use.

Oscar Orange is on top of the box of oranges. Colour his friends. Which is the odd one out?

Oo

Pp

Poor Peter wants to find matching penguins. Join each pair together with a line.

Quarrelsome Queen is making a quilt. Draw some more pieces for her quilt.

Qq

Rr

Robber Red is on the run. Help him to find his way to the raft on the river.

Sammy Snake is having
fun at the seaside.
Finish colouring this picture.
S s
1
2
2
2
3
2
2
2
1
1
1
1
1
3
Use these colours.
1
2
3

T t

Ticking Tess is talking to a tortoise on the telephone. Which one? Which tortoises are talking to each other?

Finish colouring Uppy Umbrella using the colours shown. Draw an umbrella you would like.

Draw faces on the flowers in the Vase of Violets. Finish colouring them in.

W w

What has Wicked Water Witch hung on her washing line? Join the dots to find out.

Max is giving a card to
his cousin Maxine.
Add some more kisses.

Yy

Use your
yellow crayon
to finish
Yellow Yo-yo
Man's picture.

Zz

Zig Zag Zebra has lost
some of her stripes.
Give her some new stripes.